OH MY GOD,
WHAT A COMPLETE DIARY 2022

Gill Books
Hume Avenue
Park West
Dublin 12
www.gillbooks.ie

Gill Books is an imprint of M.H. Gill & Co.
© Emer McLysaght and Sarah Breen 2021
978 07171 9270 0

Proofread by Esther Ní Dhonnacha
Designed by grahamthew.com
Printed in Turkey by the Imago Group
This book is typeset in Futura Book

This book is a work of fiction. Any references to historical events, real people or real places are used fictitiously. Other names, characters, places and incidents are products of the author's imagination, and any resemblance to actual incidents or persons, living or dead, is entirely coincidental.

The paper used in this book comes from the wood pulp of managed forests. For every tree felled, at least one tree is planted, thereby renewing natural resources.

5 4 3 2 1

THIS DIARY BELONGS TO

Also by the Authors

OH MY GOD, WHAT A COMPLETE AISLING

THE IMPORTANCE OF BEING AISLING

ONCE, TWICE, THREE TIMES AN AISLING

OH MY GOD,

What a
COMPLETE
DIARY
2022

—

EMER MCLYSAGHT & SARAH BREEN

—

GILL BOOKS

Hello, and a very happy new year!

Being organised is one of the cornerstones of Aisling's personality. But as much as she makes it look easy, it takes lots of work behind the scenes to keep track of whose turn it is to host book club or to remember when she's entitled to visit the dentist for a reduced-price scale and polish. (Isn't that why she's paying PRSI?) A good diary, like this one, is her secret weapon. Well, not-so-secret now.

We're thrilled you're taking Aisling with you into 2022, and with her a place to keep your special dates, appointments, goals, lists and plans. You have two pages per week, the all-important space for your Important Bits as well as lots of extra pages for notes and notions. You might want to keep track of the books you're reading, the beaches, towns and cities you'd like to visit, or maybe you want to take a leaf out of Majella's book and make a list of all the people who've ever wronged you. Remember when Siobhan McKenna copied your geography homework and then told the teacher it was you who copied off her? After you spending hours at it? Put her on the list, draw a peace symbol or a flower beside her name and let it go, because 2022 has no place for grudges. We've all been through enough.

Each month is introduced with an iconic and sometimes inspirational quote from a selection of Aisling's favourite people. There's also a special exclusive extract from Aisling's very own diary at the beginning of every month. Think of it as a little incentive to keep you going until the end of the year. Because we all need a little push sometimes, don't we?

We sincerely hope you love *Oh My God, What a Complete Diary 2022*, that you find it useful and, more than anything, that it brings you a little bit of joy each day. God knows we've certainly had plenty of craic putting it together.

Love,

Emer and Sarah

2022 AT A GLANCE

JANUARY

M	T	W	T	F	S	S
					1	2
3	4	5	6	7	8	9
10	11	12	13	14	15	16
17	18	19	20	21	22	23
24	25	26	27	28	29	30
31						

FEBRUARY

M	T	W	T	F	S	S
	1	2	3	4	5	6
7	8	9	10	11	12	13
14	15	16	17	18	19	20
21	22	23	24	25	26	27
28						

MARCH

M	T	W	T	F	S	S
	1	2	3	4	5	6
7	8	9	10	11	12	13
14	15	16	17	18	19	20
21	22	23	24	25	26	27
28	29	30	31			

APRIL

M	T	W	T	F	S	S
				1	2	3
4	5	6	7	8	9	10
11	12	13	14	15	16	17
18	19	20	21	22	23	24
25	26	27	28	29	30	

MAY

M	T	W	T	F	S	S
						1
2	3	4	5	6	7	8
9	10	11	12	13	14	15
16	17	18	19	20	21	22
23	24	25	26	27	28	29
30	31					

JUNE

M	T	W	T	F	S	S
		1	2	3	4	5
6	7	8	9	10	11	12
13	14	15	16	17	18	19
20	21	22	23	24	25	26
27	28	29	30			

PUBLIC HOLIDAYS 2022

1 January 2022, Saturday, New Year's Day
17 March 2022, Thursday, St Patrick's Day
18 April 2022, Monday, Easter Monday

2 May 2022, Monday, May Bank Holiday
6 June 2022, Monday, June Bank Holiday

2022 AT A GLANCE

JULY

M	T	W	T	F	S	S
				1	2	3
4	5	6	7	8	9	10
11	12	13	14	15	16	17
18	19	20	21	22	23	24
25	26	27	28	29	30	31

AUGUST

M	T	W	T	F	S	S
1	2	3	4	5	6	7
8	9	10	11	12	13	14
15	16	17	18	19	20	21
22	23	24	25	26	27	28
29	30	31				

SEPTEMBER

M	T	W	T	F	S	S
			1	2	3	4
5	6	7	8	9	10	11
12	13	14	15	16	17	18
19	20	21	22	23	24	25
26	27	28	29	30		

OCTOBER

M	T	W	T	F	S	S
					1	2
3	4	5	6	7	8	9
10	11	12	13	14	15	16
17	18	19	20	21	22	23
24	25	26	27	28	29	30
31						

NOVEMBER

M	T	W	T	F	S	S
	1	2	3	4	5	6
7	8	9	10	11	12	13
14	15	16	17	18	19	20
21	22	23	24	25	26	27
28	29	30				

DECEMBER

M	T	W	T	F	S	S
			1	2	3	4
5	6	7	8	9	10	11
12	13	14	15	16	17	18
19	20	21	22	23	24	25
26	27	28	29	30	31	

1 August 2022, Monday, August Bank Holiday
31 October 2022, Monday, October Bank Holiday

25 December 2022, Sunday, Christmas Day
26 December 2022, Monday, St Stephen's Day

2022 GOALS

2022 GOALS

HOLIDAY PLANNER

Keep track of all your plans and how many precious annual leave days
you have left.

HOLIDAY PLANNER

'You can't live a cool life with

a negative mind.'

JEDWARD

January

MONDAY	TUESDAY	WEDNESDAY
27	28	29
3	4	5
10	11	12
17	18	19
24	25	26
31	1	2

THURSDAY	FRIDAY	SATURDAY	SUNDAY
30	31	1	2
6	7	8	9
13	14	15	16
20	21	22	23
27	28	29	30
3	4	5	6

AFTER THE YEAR I tried rollerblading and ended up on a stretcher in the County General for eight hours, I swore I'd never make another New Year's resolution to try a new hobby. But then Auntie Sheila got me wool and needles for Christmas and I read an Instagram post that said knitting is great for mindfulness. Apparently, it's the new jigsaws, which were the new colouring. Even Sadhbh says knitting is having a renaissance, so I suppose I'm finally 'on trend'.

When I meet Majella for our daily post-work walk, she looks shook.

'Tadhg Timoney is still in Ballygobbard. I just saw him!'

Majella accidentally made eye contact with Tadhg Timoney on Christmas Eve.

'The cheek of him winking at me in front of my father,' she moans, pulling her high-vis vest tighter around her coat. 'And me a married woman now. I was puce going up for communion!'

That's the trouble with Midnight Mass. It's full of the ghosts of Christmas past, a.k.a. all the lads we shifted at school who've since moved away to places like Sydney and Toronto and, in Tadhg Timoney's case, Ballina.

'Jesus, it's freezing.' I pull the flaps over on my beloved Accessorize fingerless glove/mitten combos. My fifth winter with them. They were worth the investment. I wonder could I knit a pair? Might start with something a bit easier first.

'Oh, don't talk to me.' Majella increases her speed. 'The head is absolutely blown off me doing yard duty. I wonder could I sue for an ear infection?'

I choose not to indulge her.

'Did I tell you Mammy's getting an extension done?'

ALL ABOUT JANUARY

GOALS FOR JANUARY

_____

_____

_____

_____

_____

_____

_____

_____

_____

_____

_____

NEW THINGS TO READ/ WATCH/MAKE/EAT

_____

_____

_____

_____

_____

_____

_____

_____

_____

_____

_____

MUST GET DONE

_____

_____

_____

_____

_____

_____

_____

_____

_____

_____

SELF-CARE IDEAS

_____

_____

_____

_____

_____

_____

_____

_____

_____

_____

27 MONDAY DECEMBER

28 TUESDAY

29 WEDNESDAY

30 THURSDAY

31 FRIDAY NEW YEAR'S EVE

1 SATURDAY JANUARY
NEW YEAR'S DAY

2 SUNDAY

IMPORTANT BITS

M	T	W	T	F	S	S
					1	2
3	4	5	6	7	8	9
10	11	12	13	14	15	16
17	18	19	20	21	22	23
24	25	26	27	28	29	30
31						

3 MONDAY

4 TUESDAY

5 WEDNESDAY

6 THURSDAY NOLLAIG NA MBAN

*Decorations: Down! Spirits of all the
fabulous women in your life: Up!*

7 FRIDAY

8 SATURDAY
MAN WHO SLIPPED ON THE ICE ON
SIX ONE DAY

Thinking of him, always.

9 SUNDAY

IMPORTANT BITS

M	T	W	T	F	S	S
					1	2
3	4	5	6	7	8	9
10	11	12	13	14	15	16
17	18	19	20	21	22	23
24	25	26	27	28	29	30
31						

10 MONDAY

11 TUESDAY

12 WEDNESDAY

13 THURSDAY

14 FRIDAY

15 SATURDAY

16 SUNDAY

IMPORTANT BITS

M	T	W	T	F	S	S
					1	2
3	4	5	6	7	8	9
10	11	12	13	14	15	16
17	18	19	20	21	22	23
24	25	26	27	28	29	30
31						

17 **MONDAY** BLUE MONDAY

This is supposedly the saddest day of the year, so you should rebel and get McDonald's for your lunch and watch A League of Their Own under a blanket.

18 **TUESDAY**

19 **WEDNESDAY**

20 **THURSDAY**

21 **FRIDAY**

22 SATURDAY

23 SUNDAY

IMPORTANT BITS

M	T	W	T	F	S	S
					1	2
3	4	5	6	7	8	9
10	11	12	13	14	15	16
17	18	19	20	21	22	23
24	25	26	27	28	29	30
31						

24 MONDAY

25 TUESDAY

26 WEDNESDAY

27 THURSDAY

28 FRIDAY

29 SATURDAY

30 SUNDAY

IMPORTANT BITS

M	T	W	T	F	S	S
					1	2
3	4	5	6	7	8	9
10	11	12	13	14	15	16
17	18	19	20	21	22	23
24	25	26	27	28	29	30
31						

31 MONDAY

1 TUESDAY FEBRUARY

2 WEDNESDAY

3 THURSDAY

4 FRIDAY

JANUARY

5 SATURDAY

6 SUNDAY

IMPORTANT BITS

M	T	W	T	F	S	S
					1	2
3	4	5	6	7	8	9
10	11	12	13	14	15	16
17	18	19	20	21	22	23
24	25	26	27	28	29	30
31						

'Don't make unnecessary
journeys, don't take risks on
treacherous roads'

TERESA MANNION

February

FEBRUARY AT A GLANCE

MONDAY	TUESDAY	WEDNESDAY
31	1	2
7	8	9
14	15	16
21	22	23
28	1	2
7	8	9

THURSDAY	FRIDAY	SATURDAY	SUNDAY
3	4	5	6
10	11	12	13
17	18	19	20
24	25	26	27
3	4	5	6
10	11	12	13

I'M SITTING ON the couch watching an old Dermot Bannon with Mammy. He's at loggerheads with his quantity surveyor over the price of a conversation pit.

'What's the story with your utility room extension?' I ask her, before sneezing so violently that I drop three stitches. Of course, she immediately bolts for the kitchen, calling over her shoulder, 'Oh, yes, I had … someone … in looking at it. It's all systems go.'

'Mammy, would you sit down,' I call after her when I hear the rattle of a saucepan.

She comes back in with a bottle of TK Red Lemonade in her hand. 'I was just going to heat up a drop for you, pet. I'll put a Disprin in it too. You sound very bunged up.'

To be honest, I do have a Bad Cold, but I'm too old now to have Mammy waiting on me, especially after she's spent eight hours on her feet today showing a hen party from Limerick how to plough a straight furrow and dip a sheep. The eco-farm has really taken off and the yurts are fully booked from now until July. She must be wrecked.

'Here,' I say, passing her my knitting. 'You sit down there and pick up those stitches for me and I'll make us both a little hot whiskey.'

'Would you stop, I'm not having a whiskey on a Sunday night,' she says, picking up the needles. 'Well, I'll have a small one. There's a baby Powers above in the press.'

Half an hour later, Dermot is popping champagne in the conversation pit, the stitches are back in place and I'm suddenly feeling like I could lift a car off a small child.

ALL ABOUT FEBRUARY

GOALS FOR
FEBRUARY

_____
_____
_____
_____
_____
_____
_____
_____
_____
_____
_____

NEW THINGS TO READ/
WATCH/MAKE/EAT

_____
_____
_____
_____
_____
_____
_____
_____
_____
_____
_____

MUST GET DONE

_____
_____
_____
_____
_____
_____
_____
_____
_____
_____
_____

SELF-CARE IDEAS

_____
_____
_____
_____
_____
_____
_____
_____
_____
_____
_____

31 MONDAY JANUARY

1 TUESDAY ST BRIGID'S DAY

Make a cross and put it over the door to ward off evil, fire and hunger. Maybe it will also work on the junk mail that comes in, despite you buying and sticking up a sign.

2 WEDNESDAY

3 THURSDAY

4 FRIDAY

5 SATURDAY

6 SUNDAY

IMPORTANT BITS

M	T	W	T	F	S	S
	1	2	3	4	5	6
7	8	9	10	11	12	13
14	15	16	17	18	19	20
21	22	23	24	25	26	27
28						

7 MONDAY

8 TUESDAY

9 WEDNESDAY

10 THURSDAY

11 FRIDAY

12 SATURDAY

13 SUNDAY GALENTINE'S DAY

IMPORTANT BITS

M	T	W	T	F	S	S
	1	2	3	4	5	6
7	8	9	10	11	12	13
14	15	16	17	18	19	20
21	22	23	24	25	26	27
28						

14 MONDAY VALENTINE'S DAY

Book today off in an act of self-love - and to accommodate your Galentine's Day hangover. You're worth it.

15 TUESDAY

16 WEDNESDAY

17 THURSDAY

18 FRIDAY

19 SATURDAY

20 SUNDAY

IMPORTANT BITS

M	T	W	T	F	S	S
	1	2	3	4	5	6
7	8	9	10	11	12	13
14	15	16	17	18	19	20
21	22	23	24	25	26	27
28						

21 MONDAY

22 TUESDAY

23 WEDNESDAY

24 THURSDAY

25 FRIDAY

26 SATURDAY

27 SUNDAY

IMPORTANT BITS

M	T	W	T	F	S	S
	1	2	3	4	5	6
7	8	9	10	11	12	13
14	15	16	17	18	19	20
21	22	23	24	25	26	27
28						

28 MONDAY

1 TUESDAY MARCH

2 WEDNESDAY

3 THURSDAY

4 FRIDAY

5 SATURDAY

6 SUNDAY

IMPORTANT BITS

M	T	W	T	F	S	S
	1	2	3	4	5	6
7	8	9	10	11	12	13
14	15	16	17	18	19	20
21	22	23	24	25	26	27
28						

'I was elected ... by the women of Ireland, mná na hÉireann, who instead of rocking the cradle rocked the system'

MARY ROBINSON

March

MONDAY	TUESDAY	WEDNESDAY
28	1	2
7	8	9
14	15	16
21	22	23
28	29	30
4	5	6

THURSDAY	FRIDAY	SATURDAY	SUNDAY
3	4	5	6
10	11	12	13
17	18	19	20
24	25	26	27
31	1	2	3
7	8	9	10

WHEN MAJELLA SAID she had booked a weekend away for herself, myself and Sadhbh, I didn't think we'd all be sharing the same room.

'Bagsy the single bed,' Sadhbh shrieks, flinging her little overnight bag on it as soon as I open the door.

'No problem, myself and Ais are well used to sharing, aren't we, Ais?'

Of course, Maj is talking about all the sleepovers we had growing up, but what she doesn't realise is that she's a complete nightmare to share a bed with. It's not like Pablo would say anything – he never even told her the time she reversed over his foot. Yes, there's the snoring, but she thrashes around all night too, plus she has the toenails of a sloth. But feck it, it's nice to be away, even if it's only two nights in a bed and breakfast with dinner on an evening of our choice.

'We are, of course,' I sigh and commence my hotel room ritual of opening every last press and drawer in the place. I have Sadhbh doing it now too. There are two lovely armchairs in the room. Pity I didn't bring my knitting, but I've started working on a project for Maj and I didn't want to spoil the surprise.

Sadhbh whistles from across the room. 'Ooh, the hairdryer's a Dyson. Very swish.'

Maj is over in a flash. 'Is it strapped to the wall?'

'I think so.' Sadhbh gives it a jiggle. 'Feels sturdy.'

'Probably for the best,' Majella admits, opening her suitcase. 'They have my credit card number on file. Now, who's for a glass of vino?'

'Go on so,' I say, as Sadhbh flings open the balcony doors.

'Did I tell you Susan Doyle's wedding is the day before my cousin Brenda's?' I ask Maj. We went to school with Susan Doyle, but neither of us expected to be invited to her wedding. She must have gone for the 300-plate package at the Ard Rí and needs seat fillers.

Majella's not listening to me though. 'Feck it,' she mutters under her breath. 'I'm after forgetting my nightie.'

ALL ABOUT MARCH

GOALS FOR
MARCH

NEW THINGS TO READ/
WATCH/MAKE/EAT

_____

_____

_____

_____

_____

_____

_____

_____

_____

_____

_____

_____

MUST GET DONE

SELF-CARE IDEAS

_____

_____

_____

_____

_____

_____

_____

_____

_____

_____

_____

28 MONDAY FEBRUARY

1 TUESDAY **MARCH** PANCAKE TUESDAY

I always use the 3-2-1 rule: 300ml milk, 2 eggs, 100g flour. That only makes eight though, so obviously triple it. We're not animals.

2 WEDNESDAY

3 THURSDAY WORLD BOOK DAY

No Aisling costume would be complete without an 80-denier tight and at least five clips in your hair to control the flyaways.

4 FRIDAY

5 SATURDAY

6 SUNDAY

IMPORTANT BITS

M	T	W	T	F	S	S
	1	2	3	4	5	6
7	8	9	10	11	12	13
14	15	16	17	18	19	20
21	22	23	24	25	26	27
28	29	30	31			

7 MONDAY

8 TUESDAY INTERNATIONAL WOMEN'S DAY

9 WEDNESDAY

10 THURSDAY

11 FRIDAY

12 SATURDAY

13 SUNDAY

IMPORTANT BITS

M	T	W	T	F	S	S
	1	2	3	4	5	6
7	8	9	10	11	12	13
14	15	16	17	18	19	20
21	22	23	24	25	26	27
28	29	30	31			

14 MONDAY

15 TUESDAY

16 WEDNESDAY

17 **THURSDAY** ST PATRICK'S DAY   *Snakes out!*

18 FRIDAY

19 SATURDAY

20 SUNDAY

IMPORTANT BITS

M	T	W	T	F	S	S
	1	2	3	4	5	6
7	8	9	10	11	12	13
14	15	16	17	18	19	20
21	22	23	24	25	26	27
28	29	30	31			

21 MONDAY

22 TUESDAY REMINDER!

It's Mother's Day this Sunday. If you celebrate, this is your card warning.

23 WEDNESDAY

24 THURSDAY

25 FRIDAY

26 SATURDAY

27 SUNDAY
MOTHER'S DAY /
CLOCKS GO FORWARD

IMPORTANT BITS

M	T	W	T	F	S	S
	1	2	3	4	5	6
7	8	9	10	11	12	13
14	15	16	17	18	19	20
21	22	23	24	25	26	27
28	29	30	31			

28 MONDAY

29 TUESDAY

30 WEDNESDAY

31 THURSDAY

1 FRIDAY APRIL

2 SATURDAY

3 SUNDAY

IMPORTANT BITS

M	T	W	T	F	S	S
	1	2	3	4	5	6
7	8	9	10	11	12	13
14	15	16	17	18	19	20
21	22	23	24	25	26	27
28	29	30	31			

'My name's not that hard to pronounce'

DENISE CHAILA

April

MONDAY	TUESDAY	WEDNESDAY
28	29	30
4	5	6
11	12	13
18	19	20
25	26	27
2	3	4

THURSDAY	FRIDAY	SATURDAY	SUNDAY
31	1	2	3
7	8	9	10
14	15	16	17
21	22	23	24
28	29	30	1
5	6	7	8

I DON'T KNOW why everyone complains about having to do the NCT. I've always found the whole process very enjoyable and aren't the roads all the safer for it in the long run?

Even though it's only been three months since I had my Micra serviced, I drop it into Eamon Filan's garage anyway. Pablo always gives me a good deal on a pre-NCT.

'I drop it back in maybe one hour?' he says.

'Right you are, Pab.'

Two hours later, there's no sign of him and even my knitting isn't taking my mind off it. After three hours, feck it, I ring his mobile.

'Aisling, the queen of Ballygobbard!' It sounds like he's in a wind tunnel. 'I am there in one minute.' Then he hangs up.

I tip out into the yard to see if there's any sign of him and see a cloud of dust flying up from the gate. Pablo screeches to a halt in front of me, narrowly avoiding the pallet of bricks that have been sitting in the driveway for weeks now. The car is covered in about an inch of muck.

'Pablo, what the blazes happened?'

'I am sorry, Aisling, but there was an emergency. Your car, well, it saved the day!'

My hand flies to my throat. 'What happened? Is everyone okay?'

His face lights up. 'It was *mi amor*. She left for school, but she called to say she forgot her Good Pen.'

'So you drove my car to *Santry* to bring Majella a *pen*?' I'm incredulous, obviously.

'Well, it is the best maintained car in BGB,' he says.

And after that, well, I couldn't stay cross with him.

ALL ABOUT APRIL

GOALS FOR
APRIL

NEW THINGS TO READ/
WATCH/MAKE/EAT

_____

_____

_____

_____

_____

_____

_____

_____

_____

_____

MUST GET DONE

SELF-CARE IDEAS

_____

_____

_____

_____

_____

_____

_____

_____

_____

_____

28 MONDAY MARCH

29 TUESDAY

30 WEDNESDAY

31 THURSDAY

1 FRIDAY **APRIL** APRIL FOOL'S DAY

APRIL

2 SATURDAY

3 SUNDAY

IMPORTANT BITS

M	T	W	T	F	S	S
				1	2	3
4	5	6	7	8	9	10
11	12	13	14	15	16	17
18	19	20	21	22	23	24
25	26	27	28	29	30	

4 MONDAY

5 TUESDAY

6 WEDNESDAY

7 THURSDAY

8 FRIDAY

9 SATURDAY

10 SUNDAY

IMPORTANT BITS

M	T	W	T	F	S	S
				1	2	3
4	5	6	7	8	9	10
11	12	13	14	15	16	17
18	19	20	21	22	23	24
25	26	27	28	29	30	

APRIL 11–17

---

11 MONDAY

---

12 TUESDAY

---

13 WEDNESDAY

---

14 THURSDAY

---

15 FRIDAY GOOD FRIDAY

Will we ever get used to the pubs being open? No more baffled tourists, thank God. Although I do love to help a tourist.

APRIL

16 SATURDAY

17 SUNDAY EASTER SUNDAY

IMPORTANT BITS

M	T	W	T	F	S	S
				1	2	3
4	5	6	7	8	9	10
11	12	13	14	15	16	17
18	19	20	21	22	23	24
25	26	27	28	29	30	

APRIL 18–24

18 **MONDAY** BANK HOLIDAY / MICHAEL D'S BIRTHDAY

Born in April 1941 and sent by angels to teach us about poetry, nice walks and the love of a good dog: Miggeldy, the man, the myth, the legend.

19 TUESDAY

20 WEDNESDAY

21 THURSDAY

22 **FRIDAY** WORLD EARTH DAY

You might switch off a few of those lights?

23 SATURDAY

24 SUNDAY

IMPORTANT BITS

M	T	W	T	F	S	S
				1	2	3
4	5	6	7	8	9	10
11	12	13	14	15	16	17
18	19	20	21	22	23	24
25	26	27	28	29	30	

25 MONDAY

26 TUESDAY

27 WEDNESDAY

28 THURSDAY

29 FRIDAY

30 SATURDAY

1 SUNDAY MAY

IMPORTANT BITS

M	T	W	T	F	S	S
				1	2	3
4	5	6	7	8	9	10
11	12	13	14	15	16	17
18	19	20	21	22	23	24
25	26	27	28	29	30	

'Why me?'

LINDA MARTIN

May

MONDAY	TUESDAY	WEDNESDAY
25	26	27
2	3	4
9	10	11
16	17	18
23	24	25
30	31	1

MAY AT A GLANCE

THURSDAY	FRIDAY	SATURDAY	SUNDAY
28	29	30	1
5	6	7	8
12	13	14	15
19	20	21	22
26	27	28	29
2	3	4	5

AISLING'S MAY

AS SOON AS I got Susan Doyle's invite, I decided I was letting the hair grow. Two weddings in one weekend? It was like a sign from the universe to go long and really experiment with the updos. Sharon has convinced me to come into Strong Stuff for a trim though. At least I can get some knitting done.

'Now, I only want to take about half a centimetre off it,' I say sternly. I know what hairdressers are like – they have itchy scissor fingers.

'Ah Ais, you've loads of split ends. I think it'll need at least two inches to get it in good shape.'

Over my dead body. 'But that's about six months of growing.'

'I know! You haven't let me at it since before Christmas! An inch then. Go on.' She hands me a glass of Prosecco and a Lindor and I feel my resolve weakening.

'Okay, an inch so. And I have a ruler in my bag if you need it.' You'd be surprised how often it comes in handy.

Later on, I'm mashing spuds in the kitchen when Mammy comes blustering in with a box of carrots fresh from the farm shop. I must ask her about the bags of cement that have appeared out in the shed. And no ground broken yet on the extension.

'Aisling, pet, will you peel those for...' Her eyes widen when she sees me. I run a hand down the back of my hair self-consciously. 'I thought you were only getting a trim?' she gasps. 'It's above your shoulders! What about your wedding updo?'

'I know, but Sharon was right. It's much healthier now. And sure, I can always dress it up with a fascinator instead. I own enough of them.'

ALL ABOUT MAY

GOALS FOR
MAY

NEW THINGS TO READ/
WATCH/MAKE/EAT

_____
_____
_____
_____
_____
_____
_____
_____
_____
_____

MUST GET DONE

SELF-CARE IDEAS

_____
_____
_____
_____
_____
_____
_____
_____
_____
_____

25 MONDAY **APRIL**

26 TUESDAY

27 WEDNESDAY

28 THURSDAY

29 FRIDAY

30 SATURDAY

1 SUNDAY MAY

IMPORTANT BITS

M	T	W	T	F	S	S
						1
2	3	4	5	6	7	8
9	10	11	12	13	14	15
16	17	18	19	20	21	22
23	24	25	26	27	28	29
30	31					

2 **MONDAY** MAY BANK HOLIDAY

3 TUESDAY

4 WEDNESDAY

5 THURSDAY

6 FRIDAY

7 SATURDAY

8 SUNDAY

IMPORTANT BITS

M	T	W	T	F	S	S
						1
2	3	4	5	6	7	8
9	10	11	12	13	14	15
16	17	18	19	20	21	22
23	24	25	26	27	28	29
30	31					

MAY 9–15

9 **MONDAY** 30TH ANNIVERSARY OF WHY ME?

Linda Martin's iconic win in Malmö, Sweden, three decades ago set off a trio of victories for Ireland and near-financial ruin from hosting Eurovision. Worth it.

10 **TUESDAY**

11 **WEDNESDAY**

12 **THURSDAY** INTERNATIONAL NURSES DAY

As a wise man once said, 'No happy birthday to him! Up the nurses!'

13 **FRIDAY**

14 SATURDAY

15 SUNDAY

IMPORTANT BITS

M	T	W	T	F	S	S
						1
2	3	4	5	6	7	8
9	10	11	12	13	14	15
16	17	18	19	20	21	22
23	24	25	26	27	28	29
30	31					

16 MONDAY

17 TUESDAY WORLD PINOT GRIGIO DAY

Happy Pinot Greej Christmas!

18 WEDNESDAY

19 THURSDAY

20 FRIDAY

21 SATURDAY

22 SUNDAY

IMPORTANT BITS

M	T	W	T	F	S	S
						1
2	3	4	5	6	7	8
9	10	11	12	13	14	15
16	17	18	19	20	21	22
23	24	25	26	27	28	29
30	31					

MAY 23–29

23 MONDAY

24 TUESDAY

25 WEDNESDAY

26 THURSDAY

27 FRIDAY

28 SATURDAY

29 SUNDAY

IMPORTANT BITS

M	T	W	T	F	S	S
						1
2	3	4	5	6	7	8
9	10	11	12	13	14	15
16	17	18	19	20	21	22
23	24	25	26	27	28	29
30	31					

30 MONDAY

31 TUESDAY

1 WEDNESDAY JUNE

2 THURSDAY

3 FRIDAY

MAY

4 SATURDAY

5 SUNDAY

IMPORTANT BITS

M	T	W	T	F	S	S
						1
2	3	4	5	6	7	8
9	10	11	12	13	14	15
16	17	18	19	20	21	22
23	24	25	26	27	28	29
30	31					

MAY NOTES

'And remember now, you're the tops!'

BOSCO

June

MONDAY	TUESDAY	WEDNESDAY
30	31	1
6	7	8
13	14	15
20	21	22
27	28	29
4	5	6

THURSDAY	FRIDAY	SATURDAY	SUNDAY
2	3	4	5
9	10	11	12
16	17	18	19
23	24	25	26
30	1	2	3
7	8	9	10

I'VE BEEN BITING my lip for nearly three hours. I just can't do it anymore.

'This is not a staycation, it's a *holiday*,' I roar. Beside me, in the passenger seat, Sadhbh jumps with the fright. Pablo sticks his hands through the headrest from the backseat and starts massaging my shoulders. It's no wonder I'm stressed. I had to leave my knitting behind again to keep my Majella project hush hush. I had originally planned it for her birthday, but it's taking longer than expected so I'm pushing it to Christmas.

'Ssshh, Ais, it is okay.'

'Will we stick on the radio?' Majella asks. 'Maybe a podcast?'

But I'm not finished. 'A staycation is when you stay at home in your own house and do touristy stuff. Visit a dolmen or something. We're renting a house on the other side of the country. I've my togs in the boot. This is definitely a holiday.'

Sadhbh is remorseful. 'I just meant that a holiday in Ireland is not the same as going to Ibiza or somewhere, that's all,' she says quietly.

I feel bad now. 'How about I Spy?' Maj asks.

'I'd love to, lads, but I think we're lost.' This is what I get for letting them convince me to leave my road atlas at home. You just can't rely on having phone signal in the backarse of nowhere. Then I spot a man at the side of the road with a sheepdog.

'I'm going to pull in, Sadhbh. You ask him how to get to the R600 to Kinsale.'

Sadhbh rolls down the window and gives the man her friendliest smile. 'Hi there, we're looking for directions. Can you help?'

'I can, of course,' he says, shuffling over to the window. 'You're not local then?'

'No,' she beams, 'we're on a staycation.'

ALL ABOUT JUNE

GOALS FOR JUNE

_____
_____
_____
_____
_____
_____
_____
_____
_____
_____
_____
_____

NEW THINGS TO READ/ WATCH/MAKE/EAT

_____
_____
_____
_____
_____
_____
_____
_____
_____
_____
_____
_____

MUST GET DONE

_____
_____
_____
_____
_____
_____
_____
_____
_____
_____
_____

SELF-CARE IDEAS

_____
_____
_____
_____
_____
_____
_____
_____
_____
_____
_____

JUNE 1–5

30 MONDAY MAY

31 TUESDAY

1 WEDNESDAY JUNE

2 THURSDAY

3 FRIDAY

JUNE

4 SATURDAY

5 SUNDAY

IMPORTANT BITS

M	T	W	T	F	S	S
		1	2	3	4	5
6	7	8	9	10	11	12
13	14	15	16	17	18	19
20	21	22	23	24	25	26
27	28	29	30			

JUNE 6–12

6 **MONDAY** JUNE BANK HOLIDAY

7 TUESDAY

8 WEDNESDAY

9 THURSDAY

10 FRIDAY

JUNE

11 SATURDAY

12 SUNDAY

IMPORTANT BITS

M	T	W	T	F	S	S
		1	2	3	4	5
6	7	8	9	10	11	12
13	14	15	16	17	18	19
20	21	22	23	24	25	26
27	28	29	30			

---

13 MONDAY

---

14 TUESDAY REMINDER!

It's Father's Day this Sunday. If you celebrate, this is your card warning.

---

15 WEDNESDAY NADINE COYLE'S BIRTHDAY

Making her a Gemini.

---

16 THURSDAY

---

17 FRIDAY

---

18 SATURDAY

19 SUNDAY FATHER'S DAY

IMPORTANT BITS

M	T	W	T	F	S	S
		1	2	3	4	5
6	7	8	9	10	11	12
13	14	15	16	17	18	19
20	21	22	23	24	25	26
27	28	29	30			

JUNE 20–26

20 MONDAY

21 TUESDAY

22 WEDNESDAY

23 THURSDAY

24 FRIDAY

JUNE

25 SATURDAY

26 SUNDAY

IMPORTANT BITS

M	T	W	T	F	S	S
		1	2	3	4	5
6	7	8	9	10	11	12
13	14	15	16	17	18	19
20	21	22	23	24	25	26
27	28	29	30			

27 MONDAY

28 TUESDAY

29 WEDNESDAY

30 THURSDAY TOTO SCHILLACI DAY

On this day in 1990, Salvatore 'Toto' Schillaci scored the goal that knocked Ireland out of the World Cup. It keeps us humble. And raging.

1 FRIDAY JULY

JUNE

2 SATURDAY

3 SUNDAY

IMPORTANT BITS

M	T	W	T	F	S	S
		1	2	3	4	5
6	7	8	9	10	11	12
13	14	15	16	17	18	19
20	21	22	23	24	25	26
27	28	29	30			

'Life's too short, I'm going to Marbella.'

LOUISE, FADE STREET

July

MONDAY	TUESDAY	WEDNESDAY
27	28	29
4	5	6
11	12	13
18	19	20
25	26	27
1	2	3

JULY AT A GLANCE

THURSDAY	FRIDAY	SATURDAY	SUNDAY
30	1	2	3
7	8	9	10
14	15	16	17
21	22	23	24
28	29	30	31
4	5	6	7

I WENT AHEAD and made a spreadsheet. The logistics of two weddings in two days in two different counties was starting to wake me up in the sweats. I was having nightmares about bringing the wrong bra to wear with the carefully selected floral Zara dress for my cousin Brenda's big day.

I'm sitting in the hotel room fifteen minutes ahead of schedule, waiting for Mammy to hustle back from mass and zip up my dress. It's great that we're away for the night actually, because work is finally starting on the extension.

'They might get the walls up,' were Mammy's exact hopeful words.

She's been very calm and collected about the whole endeavour. It's been months!

I thought she'd be fuming that I had to miss the church but with a two-hour drive from the hotel after Susan Doyle's wedding and Mammy's lifelong commitment to telling me to go easy on the roads, she said I was 'dead right' and managed to slip in a dig about the mass probably being very boring anyway, seeing as Brenda's fiancé Michael's family own a funeral parlour.

An hour and five minutes later and I'm still waiting. Majella is sending me selfies from day two of wedding one and I can see by her eyes and general pallor that those tequilas she was ordering as I headed to bed last night were a mistake.

There's a clattering at the door and Mammy click-clacks in, fascinator in hand, ankles wobbling on the unfamiliar heels.

'Sorry, pet, sorry. There was a mix-up and a hearse arrived for the happy couple. Is that what you're wearing?'

GOALS FOR JULY

_____
_____
_____
_____
_____
_____
_____
_____
_____
_____
_____
_____

NEW THINGS TO READ/ WATCH/MAKE/EAT

_____
_____
_____
_____
_____
_____
_____
_____
_____
_____
_____

MUST GET DONE

_____
_____
_____
_____
_____
_____
_____
_____
_____
_____
_____

SELF-CARE IDEAS

_____
_____
_____
_____
_____
_____
_____
_____
_____
_____
_____

27 MONDAY JUNE

28 TUESDAY

29 WEDNESDAY

30 THURSDAY

1 FRIDAY JULY CANADA DAY

Celebrate with poutine – chips smothered in gravy and cheese curd. Maybe keep the Rennies handy for afterwards.

2 SATURDAY

3 SUNDAY

IMPORTANT BITS

M	T	W	T	F	S	S
				1	2	3
4	5	6	7	8	9	10
11	12	13	14	15	16	17
18	19	20	21	22	23	24
25	26	27	28	29	30	31

JULY 4-10

---

4 MONDAY US INDEPENDENCE DAY

Can't find your DVD of the 1996 film? Don't worry, it'll almost definitely be on RTÉ2.

---

5 TUESDAY

---

6 WEDNESDAY

---

7 THURSDAY

---

8 FRIDAY

---

9 SATURDAY

10 SUNDAY

IMPORTANT BITS

M	T	W	T	F	S	S
				1	2	3
4	5	6	7	8	9	10
11	12	13	14	15	16	17
18	19	20	21	22	23	24
25	26	27	28	29	30	31

11 MONDAY

12 TUESDAY

13 WEDNESDAY

14 THURSDAY

15 FRIDAY

16 SATURDAY

17 SUNDAY

IMPORTANT BITS

M	T	W	T	F	S	S
				1	2	3
4	5	6	7	8	9	10
11	12	13	14	15	16	17
18	19	20	21	22	23	24
25	26	27	28	29	30	31

18 MONDAY

19 TUESDAY

20 WEDNESDAY

21 THURSDAY

22 FRIDAY

23 SATURDAY

24 SUNDAY

IMPORTANT BITS

M	T	W	T	F	S	S
				1	2	3
4	5	6	7	8	9	10
11	12	13	14	15	16	17
18	19	20	21	22	23	24
25	26	27	28	29	30	31

---

25 **MONDAY** GALWAY RACES   *Who needs the Fianna Fáil tent anyway?*

---

26 TUESDAY

---

27 WEDNESDAY

---

28 THURSDAY

---

29 FRIDAY

---

30 SATURDAY

31 SUNDAY

IMPORTANT BITS

M	T	W	T	F	S	S
				1	2	3
4	5	6	7	8	9	10
11	12	13	14	15	16	17
18	19	20	21	22	23	24
25	26	27	28	29	30	31

'They say you never miss the

water until it's gone (yeah)'

WESTLIFE

August

MONDAY	TUESDAY	WEDNESDAY
25	26	27
1	2	3
8	9	10
15	16	17
22	23	24
29	30	31

THURSDAY	FRIDAY	SATURDAY	SUNDAY
28	29	30	31
4	5	6	7
11	12	13	14
18	19	20	21
25	26	27	28
1	2	3	4

'**AISLING, YOU ARE** not bringing your knitting to a festival?'

'Will they even let her in with the needles?'

'Good point. I doubt they'll even let you in with the needles.'

Sadhbh and Elaine have a point, I suppose. They could be interpreted as a weapon. It's just become such second nature that I like to be able to whip out my knitting whenever the fancy takes me. I'm deep into my Christmas project for Majella and thought I could get a good bit done sitting in my camping chair with my pink G & T in a can. Sadhbh has sorted us out with glamping so I'm feeling quite relaxed about this weekend. I haven't been to a festival in a few years and the slagging I got that time for bringing a padlock for the tent is still ringing in my ears. They weren't slagging me when their twelve packs of Chickatees were still there at 3 a.m.

'So, I don't need a sleeping bag even?' I triple check.

'Nothing. Beds and all will be set up. There's even a lamp and electrical sockets. And a mirror! We'll be like Kate Moss at Glastonbury.'

Elaine is driving so we pack our bags into the car and decant our wine into two-litre 7up bottles. I write 'WINE' on the side of mine with a permanent marker. The story of Majella having a bottle of water and a bottle of wine both with 'W' scrawled on the side at Electric Picnic one year is a cautionary tale.

Five hours later and we see Sadhbh was right. There are camp beds and duvets and even a mirror. It's a shame the door opens right onto the Portaloos though. Kate Moss wouldn't have stood for it.

ALL ABOUT AUGUST

GOALS FOR
AUGUST

_____
_____
_____
_____
_____
_____
_____
_____
_____
_____

NEW THINGS TO READ/
WATCH/MAKE/EAT

_____
_____
_____
_____
_____
_____
_____
_____
_____
_____

MUST GET DONE

_____
_____
_____
_____
_____
_____
_____
_____
_____
_____
_____

SELF-CARE IDEAS

_____
_____
_____
_____
_____
_____
_____
_____
_____
_____
_____

1 **MONDAY AUGUST** AUGUST BANK HOLIDAY

2 TUESDAY

3 WEDNESDAY

4 THURSDAY

5 FRIDAY

AUGUST

6 SATURDAY

7 SUNDAY

IMPORTANT BITS

M	T	W	T	F	S	S
1	2	3	4	5	6	7
8	9	10	11	12	13	14
15	16	17	18	19	20	21
22	23	24	25	26	27	28
29	30	31				

AUGUST 8-14

8 **MONDAY** INTERNATIONAL CAT DAY

I'll be giving The Bloody Cat the skin off my salmon darne today and double checking for kittens under my bonnet.

9 TUESDAY

10 WEDNESDAY

11 THURSDAY

12 FRIDAY

13 ^{SATURDAY}

14 ^{SUNDAY}

IMPORTANT BITS

M	T	W	T	F	S	S
1	2	3	4	5	6	7
8	9	10	11	12	13	14
15	16	17	18	19	20	21
22	23	24	25	26	27	28
29	30	31				

15 MONDAY

16 TUESDAY

17 WEDNESDAY

18 THURSDAY

19 FRIDAY

20 SATURDAY

21 SUNDAY

IMPORTANT BITS

M	T	W	T	F	S	S
1	2	3	4	5	6	7
8	9	10	11	12	13	14
15	16	17	18	19	20	21
22	23	24	25	26	27	28
29	30	31				

22 MONDAY

23 TUESDAY DUBLIN ROSE DAY

It's the 11th anniversary of the night Siobhéal Nic Eochaidh stunned the nation with her iconic hip-hop dance.

24 WEDNESDAY

25 THURSDAY

26 FRIDAY

27 SATURDAY

28 SUNDAY

IMPORTANT BITS

M	T	W	T	F	S	S
1	2	3	4	5	6	7
8	9	10	11	12	13	14
15	16	17	18	19	20	21
22	23	24	25	26	27	28
29	30	31				

29 MONDAY

30 TUESDAY

31 WEDNESDAY

1 THURSDAY SEPTEMBER

2 FRIDAY

AUGUST

IMPORTANT BITS

M	T	W	T	F	S	S
1	2	3	4	5	6	7
8	9	10	11	12	13	14
15	16	17	18	19	20	21
22	23	24	25	26	27	28
29	30	31				

AUGUST NOTES

'See ya all in Coppers'

September

MONDAY	TUESDAY	WEDNESDAY
29	30	31
5	6	7
12	13	14
19	20	21
26	27	28
3	4	5

THURSDAY	FRIDAY	SATURDAY	SUNDAY
1	2	3	4
8	9	10	11
15	16	17	18
22	23	24	25
29	30	1	2
6	7	8	9

'THAT'LL BE LOVELY, I'm sure.' The old lady in the waiting room has been dying to get chatting since I sat down, but I'm listening to one of the sleepy-time stories on my meditation app — they have Roy Keane doing them now — and clicking away with my knitting needles to calm myself so I just give her a smile and a silent 'thanks'.

I'd usually be up for small talk over the dog-eared *Hellos* and the ancient *National Geographics*, but this is the first time I'm seeing this doctor for my smear and I'm knitting like a demon to soothe my nerves. Dr Maher has been doing my smears since I turned twenty-five and, even though he's known me since I was four, at least he was a familiar face. Very cold hands but what can you do?

'Aisling?' The smiley Dr McCarthy announces my name and I nearly lose a whole line of stitches. I gather up my wool and bits and follow her into the surgery, mentally checking that I wore the most accessible downstairs clothing. Dress, tights, slip-on shoes. The last thing I need is to be fustering around with jeans or laces.

Dr McCarthy asks me the usual few questions. Then she tells me to get up on the bed and pulls the curtain across, her shiny hair swishing like a beautiful chestnut curtain across her face. Doctors just always have the shiniest hair. I sometimes lament that I never got the Points.

Shoes off, tights off, knickers off, up on the bed. Just close your eyes and think of Roy Keane.

ALL ABOUT SEPTEMBER

GOALS FOR
SEPTEMBER

_____

_____

_____

_____

_____

_____

_____

_____

_____

_____

_____

NEW THINGS TO READ/
WATCH/MAKE/EAT

_____

_____

_____

_____

_____

_____

_____

_____

_____

_____

MUST GET DONE

_____

_____

_____

_____

_____

_____

_____

_____

_____

_____

_____

SELF-CARE IDEAS

_____

_____

_____

_____

_____

_____

_____

_____

_____

_____

29 MONDAY AUGUST

30 TUESDAY

31 WEDNESDAY

1 THURSDAY SEPTEMBER

2 FRIDAY

3 SATURDAY

4 SUNDAY

IMPORTANT BITS

M	T	W	T	F	S	S
			1	2	3	4
5	6	7	8	9	10	11
12	13	14	15	16	17	18
19	20	21	22	23	24	25
26	27	28	29	30		

5 MONDAY

6 TUESDAY

7 WEDNESDAY

8 THURSDAY

9 FRIDAY

10 SATURDAY

11 SUNDAY

IMPORTANT BITS

M	T	W	T	F	S	S
			1	2	3	4
5	6	7	8	9	10	11
12	13	14	15	16	17	18
19	20	21	22	23	24	25
26	27	28	29	30		

12 MONDAY

13 TUESDAY NIALL HORAN'S BIRTHDAY

Tied with Bressie and Joe Dolan as Mullingar's finest export, Niall is 29 today.

14 WEDNESDAY

15 THURSDAY

16 FRIDAY

17 SATURDAY

18 SUNDAY

IMPORTANT BITS

M	T	W	T	F	S	S
			1	2	3	4
5	6	7	8	9	10	11
12	13	14	15	16	17	18
19	20	21	22	23	24	25
26	27	28	29	30		

19 MONDAY

20 TUESDAY

21 WEDNESDAY INTERNATIONAL DAY OF PEACE

Nothing says peace like making amends with all the girls you fell out with in secondary school. Colette Kirwan, I'm sorry for saying you were full of yourself.

22 THURSDAY

23 FRIDAY

24 SATURDAY

25 SUNDAY

IMPORTANT BITS

M	T	W	T	F	S	S
			1	2	3	4
5	6	7	8	9	10	11
12	13	14	15	16	17	18
19	20	21	22	23	24	25
26	27	28	29	30		

26 MONDAY

27 TUESDAY

28 WEDNESDAY

29 THURSDAY

30 FRIDAY

SEPTEMBER

1 SATURDAY OCTOBER

2 SUNDAY

IMPORTANT BITS

M	T	W	T	F	S	S
			1	2	3	4
5	6	7	8	9	10	11
12	13	14	15	16	17	18
19	20	21	22	23	24	25
26	27	28	29	30		

'People say "go with the flow"

but do you know what goes

with the flow? Dead fish.'

ROY KEANE

October

OCTOBER AT A GLANCE

MONDAY	TUESDAY	WEDNESDAY
26	27	28
3	4	5
10	11	12
17	18	19
24	25	26
31	1	2

THURSDAY	FRIDAY	SATURDAY	SUNDAY
29	30	1	2
6	7	8	9
13	14	15	16
20	21	22	23
27	28	29	30
3	4	5	6

IT'S TO BE the coldest Halloween on record but I'm not sure it's the best time to tell Mammy that the hole in the wall in the utility room, which has been there since July, is going to be a problem. She's gone very silent about the whole project.

I've already told Majella I'm not going with her to the party if she's going to insist on her sexy Shrek costume. I'm already very against purchased Halloween outfits and when they're a blatant attempt at being sexy on top of that, I just think it makes a mockery of the whole thing. Maj argues that the green body paint isn't a bit sexy, but I've seen *Shrek* at least twenty times and he absolutely wasn't wearing a push-up bra and bodycon burlap sack. Besides, Majella promised me she'd be the Sabina to my Michael D Higgins. She's a good half a foot taller than me and I'll put her in her highest heels.

I haven't done Halloween in BGB for a few years but there's a charity night in Maguire's and I need Majella's height to make my Michael D believable, seeing as I'm a good bit taller than him. I've been practising my little bow and shuffle and reciting some 'Wild Swans at Coole' in a Galway accent. Niamh From Across the Road is in town too and, while she beat my Chest of Drawers costume (knickers pinned onto my T-shirt) at the 2004 Halloween parade with her Passion of the Christ get-up (purchased in a shop), she's not going to take me down again.

'Can I at least open a few buttons on Sabina's blouse?' Majella complains, adjusting her pearl necklace.

'Have some respect!' I hiss at her, putting on the bald cap I fashioned out of some tights and grey wool. 'She's our Michelle Obama!'

ALL ABOUT OCTOBER

GOALS FOR OCTOBER

_____
_____
_____
_____
_____
_____
_____
_____
_____
_____

NEW THINGS TO READ/ WATCH/MAKE/EAT

_____
_____
_____
_____
_____
_____
_____
_____
_____
_____

MUST GET DONE

_____
_____
_____
_____
_____
_____
_____
_____
_____
_____

SELF-CARE IDEAS

_____
_____
_____
_____
_____
_____
_____
_____
_____
_____

26 MONDAY SEPTEMBER

27 TUESDAY

28 WEDNESDAY

29 THURSDAY

30 FRIDAY

1 SATURDAY OCTOBER

2 SUNDAY

IMPORTANT BITS

M	T	W	T	F	S	S
					1	2
3	4	5	6	7	8	9
10	11	12	13	14	15	16
17	18	19	20	21	22	23
24	25	26	27	28	29	30
31						

3 MONDAY

4 TUESDAY

5 WEDNESDAY WORLD TEACHERS' DAY

After a hard day teaching caol le caol agus leathan le leathan, the least I can do is treat Maj to a new scented candle.

6 THURSDAY

7 FRIDAY

8 SATURDAY

9 SUNDAY

IMPORTANT BITS

M	T	W	T	F	S	S
					1	2
3	4	5	6	7	8	9
10	11	12	13	14	15	16
17	18	19	20	21	22	23
24	25	26	27	28	29	30
31						

10 MONDAY

11 TUESDAY

12 WEDNESDAY

13 THURSDAY

14 FRIDAY

15 SATURDAY

16 SUNDAY

IMPORTANT BITS

M	T	W	T	F	S	S
					1	2
3	4	5	6	7	8	9
10	11	12	13	14	15	16
17	18	19	20	21	22	23
24	25	26	27	28	29	30
31						

17 MONDAY

18 TUESDAY

19 WEDNESDAY

20 THURSDAY

21 FRIDAY

22 SATURDAY

23 SUNDAY

IMPORTANT BITS

M	T	W	T	F	S	S
					1	2
3	4	5	6	7	8	9
10	11	12	13	14	15	16
17	18	19	20	21	22	23
24	25	26	27	28	29	30
31						

OCTOBER 24–30

24 MONDAY

25 TUESDAY

26 WEDNESDAY

27 THURSDAY

28 FRIDAY CLOCKS GO BACK THIS WEEKEND!

Ideas I have for using my extra hour include cleaning out my underwear drawer, finding a better deal on car insurance and descaling the kettle. You can't beat the gift of time.

29 SATURDAY

30 SUNDAY CLOCKS GO BACK

IMPORTANT BITS

M	T	W	T	F	S	S
					1	2
3	4	5	6	7	8	9
10	11	12	13	14	15	16
17	18	19	20	21	22	23
24	25	26	27	28	29	30
31						

31 **MONDAY** HALLOWEEN / OCTOBER BANK HOLIDAY

1 TUESDAY NOVEMBER

2 WEDNESDAY

3 THURSDAY

4 FRIDAY

OCTOBER

IMPORTANT BITS

M	T	W	T	F	S	S
					1	2
3	4	5	6	7	8	9
10	11	12	13	14	15	16
17	18	19	20	21	22	23
24	25	26	27	28	29	30
31						

'Won't blame it on myself, I'll

blame it on the weatherman'

B*WITCHED

November

MONDAY	TUESDAY	WEDNESDAY
31	1	2
7	8	9
14	15	16
21	22	23
28	29	30
5	6	7

THURSDAY	FRIDAY	SATURDAY	SUNDAY
3	4	5	6
10	11	12	13
17	18	19	20
24	25	26	27
1	2	3	4
8	9	10	11

I NEARLY CRASH the car into Ballygobbard's pride and joy, the new pedestrian traffic lights, and what would Tessie Daly have done then? Paid the increase in my insurance premium for the next ten years until I get my no-claims bonus back to perfect?

It would be Tessie's fault after all. She's gone absolutely buck wild with Tidy Towns power and erected an absolutely lethal set of Christmas lights across Main Street and Halloween is barely behind us. You must be able to see them from the International Space Station. The Great Wall of China has nothing on Tessie Daly's neon 'Nollaig Shona from BGB'.

'She's after using hanging basket and moss removal money, mark my words!' Mammy is raging too when I bring the news home to her. 'She was supposed to get the generic snowflakes and bells, not the custom lettering.' I can tell there have been fierce debates in the weekly meetings over this. 'And they weren't supposed to go up until the twenty-first of this month.'

Mammy is practically foaming at the mouth and I wonder is this less to do with Tessie and the lights and more to do with the argument she's having with the county council – cars have been flying past the front gate since Mad Tom knocked down both the speed limit sign and the Concealed Entrance sign coming home steaming drunk from Maguire's one night. He wasn't even driving. He was walking.

I pull my knitting out and Mammy's eyes flit over it just as the tarp on the utility room 'extension' flaps in the wind.

'Is that still Majella's present you're working on? Jesus, you're putting some elbow grease into it. She'll be thrilled.'

She better be.

ALL ABOUT NOVEMBER

GOALS FOR
NOVEMBER

NEW THINGS TO READ/
WATCH/MAKE/EAT

MUST GET DONE

SELF-CARE IDEAS

3 1

1 TUESDAY **NOVEMBER** WORLD VEGAN DAY

It would be remiss of a farmer's daughter to even consider veganism, but I've been known to enjoy a meat-free sausage or two. I draw the line at Sadhbh's nut milk though.

2 WEDNESDAY

3 THURSDAY

4 FRIDAY

5 SATURDAY

6 SUNDAY

IMPORTANT BITS

M	T	W	T	F	S	S
	1	2	3	4	5	6
7	8	9	10	11	12	13
14	15	16	17	18	19	20
21	22	23	24	25	26	27
28	29	30				

7 MONDAY

8 TUESDAY

9 WEDNESDAY

10 THURSDAY

11 FRIDAY

12 SATURDAY

13 SUNDAY

IMPORTANT BITS

M	T	W	T	F	S	S
	1	2	3	4	5	6
7	8	9	10	11	12	13
14	15	16	17	18	19	20
21	22	23	24	25	26	27
28	29	30				

14 MONDAY

15 TUESDAY

16 WEDNESDAY

17 THURSDAY

18 FRIDAY

NOVEMBER

---

19 SATURDAY

---

20 SUNDAY

IMPORTANT BITS

M	T	W	T	F	S	S
	1	2	3	4	5	6
7	8	9	10	11	12	13
14	15	16	17	18	19	20
21	22	23	24	25	26	27
28	29	30				

21 **MONDAY** WORLD TELEVISION DAY

Not paying your television licence is akin to pirating music and films. You wouldn't steal a car, would you?

22 TUESDAY

23 WEDNESDAY

24 THURSDAY

25 FRIDAY

26 SATURDAY

27 SUNDAY

IMPORTANT BITS

M	T	W	T	F	S	S
	1	2	3	4	5	6
7	8	9	10	11	12	13
14	15	16	17	18	19	20
21	22	23	24	25	26	27
28	29	30				

28 MONDAY

29 TUESDAY

30 WEDNESDAY

1 THURSDAY DECEMBER

2 FRIDAY

NOVEMBER

3 SATURDAY

4 SUNDAY

IMPORTANT BITS

M	T	W	T	F	S	S
	1	2	3	4	5	6
7	8	9	10	11	12	13
14	15	16	17	18	19	20
21	22	23	24	25	26	27
28	29	30				

'Through a chink too wide

there comes in no wonder'

PATRICK KAVANAGH, 'ADVENT'

December

MONDAY	TUESDAY	WEDNESDAY
28	29	30
5	6	7
12	13	14
19	20	21
26	27	28
2	3	4

DECEMBER AT A GLANCE

THURSDAY	FRIDAY	SATURDAY	SUNDAY
1	2	3	4
8	9	10	11
15	16	17	18
22	23	24	25
29	30	31	1
5	6	7	8

ME AND MAJELLA are doing our traditional present exchange in the back of the church before Midnight Mass kicks off at half eight.

'Smelly soaps from The Body Shop!' I'm thrilled. I'm one of the few people who genuinely appreciates them. 'And, OH MY GOD, YOU GOT ONE! A Colette Green limited edition NCT disc holder!' They've been sold out for months.

'Okay, my turn!' Majella rips the wrapping paper off the first part of her present. A powerful little torch to keep in her handbag for when she drops her phone and then can't use the phone torch to look for it.

'Thanks a million, Ais.'

'Keep going, there's more.'

But before she gets to the best part, Sergeant Foley from Knock steps out onto the pulpit and taps the microphone. There's a gasp from the congregation.

'Mad Tom, are you down there?' he asks sternly.

An arm goes up about two pews in front of us. 'What are you after me for now?' Tom shouts up brazenly.

'The rogue extension business, Tom. Meet me out the front.'

In a pew across the way I see Mammy sinking down in her seat. She was had by Mad Tom doing extensions! The bloody Dermot Bannon effect. She'll never live it down. Majella resumes her ripping. 'Oh! Oh! Oh!' The three ohs go from excited to quizzical to confused and she holds up my pride and joy.

'It's a balaclava! For when you're on yard duty! You said you're always freezing.'

'Gorgeous, Ais! It's got a lovely ... pattern'

Luckily, some of the dropped stitches ended up looking deliberate. I glance across the aisle and see none other than Tadhg Timoney looking for a seat.

'Sketch. Tadhg Timoney in his good coat,' I hiss. Within half a second, Maj has the balaclava on and is singing along to 'O Come All Ye Faithful' incognito. A Christmas miracle!

ALL ABOUT DECEMBER

GOALS FOR
DECEMBER

NEW THINGS TO READ/
WATCH/MAKE/EAT

_____
_____
_____
_____
_____
_____
_____
_____
_____
_____
_____

MUST GET DONE

SELF-CARE IDEAS

_____
_____
_____
_____
_____
_____
_____
_____
_____
_____
_____

DECEMBER 1–4

28 MONDAY NOVEMBER

29 TUESDAY

30 WEDNESDAY

1 THURSDAY DECEMBER

2 FRIDAY

3 SATURDAY

4 SUNDAY

IMPORTANT BITS

M	T	W	T	F	S	S
			1	2	3	4
5	6	7	8	9	10	11
12	13	14	15	16	17	18
19	20	21	22	23	24	25
26	27	28	29	30	31	

DECEMBER 5–11

5 MONDAY

6 TUESDAY

7 WEDNESDAY

8 THURSDAY

9 FRIDAY

10 SATURDAY

11 SUNDAY

IMPORTANT BITS

M	T	W	T	F	S	S
			1	2	3	4
5	6	7	8	9	10	11
12	13	14	15	16	17	18
19	20	21	22	23	24	25
26	27	28	29	30	31	

12 MONDAY

13 TUESDAY

14 WEDNESDAY

15 THURSDAY

16 FRIDAY

DECEMBER

17 SATURDAY

18 SUNDAY

IMPORTANT BITS

M	T	W	T	F	S	S
			1	2	3	4
5	6	7	8	9	10	11
12	13	14	15	16	17	18
19	20	21	22	23	24	25
26	27	28	29	30	31	

19 MONDAY

20 TUESDAY

21 WEDNESDAY WINTER SOLSTICE

*The shortest day, the longest night -
it's the perfect time to finish wrapping
those Christmas presents.*

22 THURSDAY

23 FRIDAY

24 **SATURDAY** CHRISTMAS EVE

25 **SUNDAY** CHRISTMAS DAY

IMPORTANT BITS

M	T	W	T	F	S	S
			1	2	3	4
5	6	7	8	9	10	11
12	13	14	15	16	17	18
19	20	21	22	23	24	25
26	27	28	29	30	31	

2 6   **MONDAY** ST STEPHEN'S DAY

Every year I threaten to have a first run at the sales, and every year I end up in Maguire's with Majella counting new handbags and engagement rings on Instagram instead.

2 7   TUESDAY

2 8   WEDNESDAY

2 9   THURSDAY

3 0   FRIDAY

DECEMBER

---

31 **SATURDAY** NEW YEAR'S EVE

1 SUNDAY **JANUARY** NEW YEAR'S DAY

IMPORTANT BITS

M	T	W	T	F	S	S
			1	2	3	4
5	6	7	8	9	10	11
12	13	14	15	16	17	18
19	20	21	22	23	24	25
26	27	28	29	30	31	

DECEMBER NOTES

FAVOURITE BOOKS AND MOVIES OF 2022

PRIORITIES FOR 2023